A Midsummer Night's Dream

William Shakespeare

Academic Industries, Inc.

West Haven, Connecticut 06516

ISBN 0-88301-766-0

Published by
Academic Industries, Inc.
The Academic Building
Saw Mill Road
West Haven, Connecticut 06516

Printed in the United States of America

about the author

William Shakespeare was born on April 23, 1564, in Stratford-on-Avon, England, the third child of John Shakespeare, a well-to-do merchant, and Mary Arden, his wife. Young William probably attended the Stratford grammar school, where he learned English, Greek, and a great deal of Latin.

In 1582 Shakespeare married Anne Hathaway. By 1583 the couple had a daughter, Susanna, and two years later the twins, Hamnet and Judith. Somewhere between 1585 and 1592 Shakespeare went to London, where he became first an actor and then a playwright. His acting company, The King's Men, appeared most often in the Globe theatre, a part of which Shakespeare himself owned.

In all, Shakespeare is believed to have written thirty-seven plays, several nondramatic poems, and a number of sonnets. In 1611 when he left the active life of the theatre, he returned to Stratford and became a country gentleman, living in the second-largest house in town. For five years he lived a quiet life. Then, on April 23, 1616, William Shakespeare died and was buried in Trinity Church in Stratford. From his own time to the present, Shakespeare is considered one of the greatest writers of the English-speaking world.

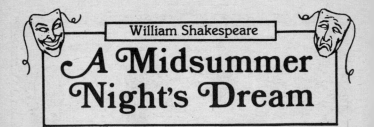

A Midsummer Night's Dream

William Shakespeare

Theseus

Lysander

Bottom

Demetrius

Helena

Hermia

Oberon

Titania

A midsummer night . . . a magic forest . . . anything could happen! Men could be changed to donkeys and ladies could fall in love with them.

Was it magic? A joke? Or was it all a dream?

These things happened long ago in Greece. At that time, Theseus, Duke of Athens, was about to marry Hippolyta, the Amazon queen.

Four days until our wedding! How can I wait so long?

The time will pass quickly, my love!

Tell my people to be happy for us! Let no one be sad!

I met you on the battlefield, my dear, but I will marry you in a happier time and place!

As Theseus was speaking, an old man came in with his daughter. Two young men followed them.

My lord duke!

Welcome, Egeus. Do you have news for me?

Yes, sir. It is my daughter Hermia.

It is my wish . . . my *command* . . . that Hermia marry Demetrius!

He is a fine young man.

Besides, you must obey your father.

But I love Lysander, who is also a fine young man!

At first Demetrius loved my best friend, Helena. He won her heart, but now he wishes to break it— and mine—by marrying *me*!

The law says a daughter must marry the man her father chooses for her—or die!

You have four days to think it over.

On my wedding day, you will tell me what you have chosen. Let us go, Hippolyta.

Soon the unhappy couple were left alone.

Don't look so sad, my love. I have a plan!

I have an aunt who lives where the laws of Athens cannot touch us. We'll go there and be married!

Leave your father's house to-morrow night. I'll wait for you in the forest, at the place where I once met you with Helena!

I'll be there!

Look, here comes Helena. When you are gone, perhaps Demetrius will love her again!

Greetings, Helena.

Oh, Hermia! I thought you were my friend! Why did you steal Demetrius away from me?

I didn't, Helena! He loves me, but I don't love him.

And the more I love him, the more he hates me.

Don't worry, dear friend. Lysander and I are going to run away!

We're meeting in the forest tomorrow night.

The lovers walked away, but Helena could think only of Demetrius.

I will tell Demetrius about this, and he will follow them. I will stay close to him!

Meanwhile, the people of Athens were planning ways to celebrate Theseus' wedding. One group of workmen decided to put on a play. They met at the house of Peter Quince, a carpenter.

What play shall we do?

A very serious play . . . Pyramus and Thisby.

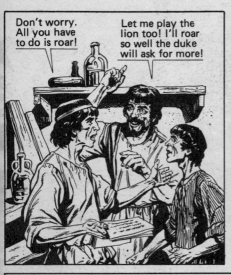

Don't worry. All you have to do is roar!

Let me play the lion too! I'll roar so well the duke will ask for more!

No, Bottom, you'd scare the ladies.

Here are your parts. Learn them well—and we will meet tomorrow night in the forest to rehearse.

We'll be there.

The next night, the young lovers went to the forest. So did the actors. But the elves and fairies were there ahead of them.

Where are you going, Spirit?

Wherever my fairy queen Titania tells me to go!

Oberon, the king of the fairies, will be here tonight. He and the queen Titania have had an argument. You'd better keep her away from here!

Titania has a lovely servant boy whom she stole from an Indian king. Oberon wants the boy as his *own* servant.

But the queen will not give him up. Oberon is very angry!

Wait—how long do you plan to stay in the forest?

Until after Theseus' wedding day.

You may come with us, if you like.

Not unless you give me that new serving boy.

Not for all the world! Come, fairies, away from this part of the forest!

Go, then . . . but you'll be sorry later!

Its magic juice will make a sleeping person fall in love with the first creature he sees when he awakes.

I'll be back in a flash!

I'll put some on Titania's eyes tonight. And I won't remove the spell until she gives me the boy!

I hear human voices! Since I am invisible to them, I'll stay and listen!

The voice belonged to Demetrius, who had come to the forest after Lysander and Hermia. Following him was poor Helena.

Demetrius, wait!

You said I would find Lysander and Hermia here! When I do, I'll kill Lysander!

19

Just then Puck returned.

Here is the flower you wanted.

Good! Give it to me.

I will find the spot where my fairy queen sleeps . . . and squeeze the juice onto her eyelids.

Meanwhile, Puck . . . take some of this and look for a handsome young man in Athenian clothes. He is somewhere nearby.

Squeeze the juice into his eyes so he will see and love the lady who loves him.

I will do as you say!

Then the fairy king crept softly to where Queen Titania slept.

I hope the first creature she sees is very ugly. That will suit my plan just right!

Meanwhile, not far away, Hermia and Lysander walked together through the woods.

My love, I'm afraid we're lost!

And I am very tired.

We'll rest here until daylight. Then we should be able to find our way.

All right. I'll sleep here. You can rest under that tree.

If my love for you ever stops . . . I hope that I will die!

22

Soon Puck came along with the magic flower.

Ah! Here's the handsome young man in Athenian clothes.

And over there sleeps the poor lady he doesn't love. Well, I'll fix that!

I've done my work. Now I must get back to Oberon.

And so, by mistake, Puck put the magic juice onto the wrong man's eyes.

Just then Demetrius rushed by, still chased by Helena.

Demetrius . . . I love you! Please don't run away!

But Demetrius was gone.

It's no use. He runs too fast, and I am out of breath.

Then she saw the sleeping Lysander.

It's Lysander! Lysander, please wake up and help me!

Hearing a voice, Lysander woke up . . . saw Helena . . . and the magic love-charm worked!

I love you, Helena! I would run through fire for you!

Where is Demetrius? I will kill him so I can have you for *myself*!

No, no!

Not knowing of the magic charm, Helena thought Lysander was joking.

Isn't it enough that Demetrius doesn't love me? Must *you* make fun of me too?

I thought you were kinder than that! I know you love Hermia.

No longer! Now *you* fill my heart, Helena!

Completely surprised by this turn of events, Helena ran away. Lysander followed her. Soon Hermia awoke.

Oh, what a bad dream I had!

Help, Lysander! What? He's gone! I must find him!

So Hermia ran into the woods after Lysander.

Meanwhile, the workmen had arrived to practice their play. By chance, they picked a place near the spot where Queen Titania was sleeping.

This will be our stage.

Wait! Before we start, there are things in the play that we must change!

The lover . . . that's me . . . must kill himself. The ladies won't like that!

True! We must leave out the killing.

No, no! But Quince must first tell them that it is only acting—that I don't really die.

All right, that's easy.

And what about the lion? A lion among ladies is a terrible thing!

That's easy, too. Quince must say that it's only a make-believe lion!

While the actors were discussing their play, Puck came by. His magic, however, kept them from seeing him—or the sleeping fairy queen.

What's all this?

Sweet Thisby, I love you dearly!

But hark, a voice! I'll return when we can be alone.

This gives me a wild idea!

Quick as a wink, while Bottom was offstage, Puck changed Bottom's head into a donkey's. So when Bottom appeared again. . . .

Fair Thisby, dear Thisby. . . .

Oh! Oh! It's a magic spell!

What is this—some kind of a trick to scare me?

They can't make a donkey out of *me*! I'll sing to show them I'm not afraid!

29

When Bottom brayed like a donkey, it woke the fairy queen . . . and the love spell worked again.

Hee . . haw!

Whose sweet voice wakes me from my dreams?

The same magic that had given Bottom a donkey's head now made it possible for him to see Titania.

Gentle being, sing again! I swear I love you!

There's no reason for that! But now that I think of it, when *do* love and reason go together?

Yes, sleep if you wish, and I will stay and admire your beauty!

Meanwhile, as Bottom slept, Puck hurried to find Oberon.

Has Titania awakened? And what was it she saw first?

She awoke—and is now in love with a monster!

Some actors were practicing a play to give on Theseus' wedding day. Queen Titania was sleeping nearby.

I changed one actor's head into a donkey's. He frightened the others, and made them run away. Right after that, Titania woke up and fell in love with him!

Well done! Did you find the young man I told you about?

Yes. I put the drops on his eyes while he slept.

But look, here comes the man now.

Oh, no! That's the woman, but it's not the same man!

Because they were invisible to humans, Puck and Oberon could listen to what Demetrius and Hermia were saying.

But I *love* you, Hermia!

I *don't* love *you*! Where is Lysander? Have you killed him in his sleep? If so, kill me too!

He is not fickle like you. He's as true to me as the sun is to the day!

33

I have not hurt Lysander!

I hate you just the same! I never want to see you again!

With that, Hermia rushed off.

Demetrius, tired from walking, lay down and was soon fast asleep.

Puck, you've made a mistake! You've put the drops on the wrong man's eyes!

We must fix things! Find Helena and bring her here. I'll make Demetrius fall in love with her again.

I'll go, swifter than an arrow!

Quickly Oberon crushed another petal and let the drops fall on Demetrius' eyes.

Now Helena will have her lover back.

Soon Puck returned, followed by Helena. Lysander was just behind her.

What a mix-up! Here comes Helena . . . and chasing her is the wrong man. What fools these mortals are!

Hearing voices, Demetrius woke with the drops on his eyes. The first person he saw was Helena.

Oh, sweet Helena! You are a goddess! How I love you!

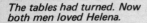

The tables had turned. Now both men loved Helena.

Leave Helena alone, Demetrius. You are in love with Hermia!

Lysander, keep your Hermia! I don't love her any longer.

Why do you keep making fun of me? If you were gentlemen, you would not do so!

And then Hermia arrived.

Lysander, sweet love, why did you leave me?

How could I *stay* with you? I had to follow the one I truly love.

W-what? *Who?*

Saying this, Demetrius and Lysander went off into the forest.

This trouble is all your fault!

I don't want to fight you, Hermia. I'll run away, and you won't catch me!

Nearby, Oberon and Puck watched what was happening.

Oh, Puck, what a mess you've made of things!

Believe me, it was only a mistake!

Now the men are looking for a place to fight. Go and cover the forest with fog so they can't find each other.

Tire them out and make sure they fall asleep . . . out of each other's way.

Then put some of this juice into Lysander's eyes. That way, when he awakes, he'll go back to his own true love.

Meanwhile, I'll see what's happening to Titania.

By now she'll be ready to give me the Indian boy. Then I'll remove the magic spell and everything will be peaceful again.

We must do these things quickly, sir. It is almost morning!

As Puck flew through the forest, he covered everything in his path with fog. Then he went to look for Lysander and Demetrius.

Up and down, all around, I will lead them up and down. —Ah! Here comes one of them!

To confuse the men, Puck spoke to each one with the voice of the other.

Demetrius, you coward! Where are you?

Here I am. Follow me, if you can!

Then he flew to Demetrius.

Lysander, you coward. Stand and fight!

I am ready. Catch me if you can!

Back and forth Puck flew, leading the men in circles. At last Lysander could go no farther.

It's useless. He runs and calls me on, but when I reach the spot, he is gone.

So Lysander lay down and fell asleep.

That's one!

Then Puck found Demetrius again.

Ho, ho, ho! Coward, come and fight!

You shall pay . . . if ever I see your face by day!

Soon Demetrius was so tired that he, too, lay down and slept.

That's two!

When the lovers were all asleep, Puck went over to Lysander and squeezed the magic juice onto his eyelids.

When he wakes up, he'll be in love with his own sweetheart again!

Then Puck went to Oberon, who had got his wish. Queen Titania had given him the Indian boy. But she was still under the magic spell.

Welcome, good Puck! The night is almost over, and soon it will seem that all that has happened was only a dream!

Then he freed Queen Titania from the magic of Cupid's flower.

Now wake, my sweet queen, and be your true self again!

45

Meanwhile, as the sun rose, Duke Theseus and Hippolyta, soon to be his wife, led their people into the forest for the beginning of their wedding festivities.

Wait! What have we here?

That's my daughter Hermia!

And these are Lysander, Demetrius, and Helena! How strange!

No doubt they heard of our plans and got up early to join us.

But isn't this the day Hermia must tell us what she will do about Demetrius?

It is, sir.

Sound your horns and wake up the sleepers!

Ta-ra-ta-ra!

Sir, Helena told me of their plan and I followed them here in anger.

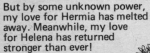

But by some unknown power, my love for Hermia has melted away. Meanwhile, my love for Helena has returned stronger than ever!

Now I wish the greatest happiness for Hermia and Lysander! And I want to marry Helena!

This is good fortune! I invite both couples to come to the temple. They will be married at the same time I marry Hippolyta!

And so the whole group returned to Athens together.

While this was happening, Bottom woke in the forest, alone.

Where am I? Where has everyone gone? They've run away and left me asleep!

What a dream I've had! I'll get Peter Quince to write a song about it.

Meanwhile, the actors had come together at Quince's house. They were upset by what had happened to Bottom.

Any news of Bottom?

No, he never came home! What will we do?

I don't know. No one else could play the part of Pyramus so well!

Just then. . . .

What are you waiting for? You should be dressed for the play!

Oh, Bottom! This is a most happy hour!

I have seen wonders. Just don't ask me what they were!

But come quickly! Get your costumes! The duke is waiting for us at the palace!

By this time the three couples were already married. At the duke's palace, the wedding feast was beginning.

The story these young lovers tell is very strange, Theseus.

Perhaps more strange than true. But you know how love is . . . it can make us believe our dreams!

Ah, here they come! May joy and happy days fill your life together!

And yours as well, sir!

Be seated, good friends. Let us see what the master of ceremonies has planned for us.

Sir, a group of simple workmen will present a play. They say it is a very sad one, too.

We'll hear it!

So Peter Quince stepped forward to introduce the play.

We come with good will to show our simple skill. We are hard-working men, not actors, but we will do our best to please you.

And so the play began.

As you know, I am a wall. I have a handy chink through which the lovers whisper.

Then Pyramus entered.

I hope my Thisby doesn't forget her promise to meet me here.

At this, Thisby entered from the other side of the wall.

Oh, wall, why do you keep me from my love?

I see a voice! I hear my Thisby's face!

Thisby!   My love!

58

Then, from its hiding place, the lion leaped.

A lion! Help!

That was a good roar, lion! But here comes Pyramus.

You'd better run away!

Thisby should be nearby. But what's this? Her torn and bloody coat!

Oh, no! A lion must have eaten her!

I can't live without her! I'll take my life with my own trusty sword!

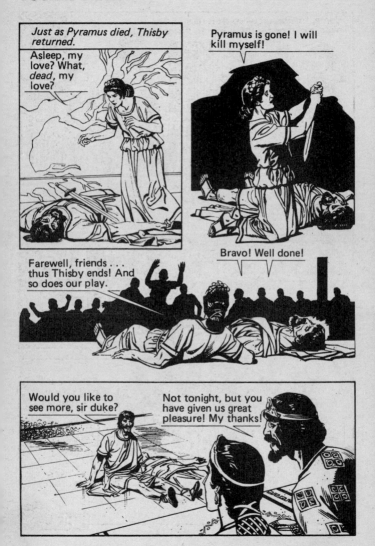

Come, friends, let us go. It is past midnight and time for the fairies to dance.

No sooner had the wedding party left, than Oberon and Titania arrived.

Hand in hand with fairy grace/Let us sing and bless this place.

From now until the break of day/Through this hall let fairies play!

Finally our play is ended, The mistakes have all been mended. And if you don't believe our theme, Think of this—'twas just a dream!

THE END

COMPLETE LIST OF POCKET CLASSICS AVAILABLE

CLASSICS

C 1 Black Beauty
C 2 The Call of the Wild
C 3 Dr. Jekyll and Mr. Hyde
C 4 Dracula
C 5 Frankenstein
C 6 Huckleberry Finn
C 7 Moby Dick
C 8 The Red Badge of Courage
C 9 The Time Machine
C10 Tom Sawyer
C11 Treasure Island
C12 20,000 Leagues Under the Sea
C13 The Great Adventures of Sherlock Holmes
C14 Gulliver's Travels
C15 The Hunchback of Notre Dame
C16 The Invisible Man
C17 Journey to the Center of the Earth
C18 Kidnapped
C19 The Mysterious Island
C20 The Scarlet Letter
C21 The Story of My Life
C22 A Tale of Two Cities
C23 The Three Musketeers
C24 The War of the Worlds
C25 Around the World in Eighty Days
C26 Captains Courageous
C27 A Connecticut Yankee in King Arthur's Court
C28 The Hound of the Baskervilles
C29 The House of the Seven Gables
C30 Jane Eyre
C31 The Last of the Mohicans
C32 The Best of O. Henry
C33 The Best of Poe
C34 Two Years Before the Mast
C35 White Fang
C36 Wuthering Heights
C37 Ben Hur
C38 A Christmas Carol
C39 The Food of the Gods
C40 Ivanhoe
C41 The Man in the Iron Mask
C42 The Prince and the Pauper
C43 The Prisoner of Zenda
C44 The Return of the Native
C45 Robinson Crusoe
C46 The Scarlet Pimpernel

COMPLETE LIST OF POCKET CLASSICS AVAILABLE
(cont'd)

SHAKESPEARE